This book belongs to

....

....

A story for classroom
teachers and students
to show how each of our
own behaviors in school
can impact and affect the
emotions and learning of
those around us.

ISBN: 978-0-578-35779-9

Written by
Samantha Shields

Daisy's
UnPerfect
School
Year

illustrated by Marija Popović

This is a story about a girl named **Daisy**.

Daisy was a **bright** student entering the first grade.

She hadn't had a '**normal school year**' yet like most kids her age because she had begun her journey in school during a time where, none other than, a pandemic had struck; causing all school learning to be conducted online.

She was beyond excited to attend school in the school building where she would spend her days ...

listening to stories being read aloud,

playing games with her friends,

learning about new things,

and best of all – being in a place she saw as a home away from home.

Daisy wasn't bothered by having to wear face masks on a daily basis, or having to use gobs of hand sanitizer throughout the day, or even having to stay distanced from her friends.

You see,
all she cared about was being among other kids
her age that she could learn alongside.

9

Not too long after school started,
Daisy began to notice that returning
to school with other friends wasn't like
what she envisioned it would be.

Daisy envisioned ...

sitting with her friends perfectly on the carpet, while listening to the teacher read aloud a book about her favorite animals ...

...but what Daisy experienced was ...

a daily attempt to listen to a story about animals that her teacher Ms. Landon **tirelessly** tried to get through

while destructive student repeatedly

slammed
slammed
slammed

the classroom door and **blurted out** words and phrases her parents taught her were inappropriate for kids her age to say.

Daisy envisioned ...

walking through the hallways 2 by 2, like the characters in her Madeline books at home, as they headed towards the cafeteria for lunch.

... but what Daisy experienced was ...

being one of the only 5 students in her class that understood the hallways were a **quiet-walking place**, not a race track for students to **run** through.

Daisy envisioned ...

playing side by side with
her friends while in gym class ...

16

...but what Daisy experienced was ...

fear of being hit, fear of being bit, and fear of witnessing a friend enduring the same pain.

She didn't understand why children her age found it funny to hurt others.

Daisy envisioned ...

working at table groups on
a project with her classmates ...

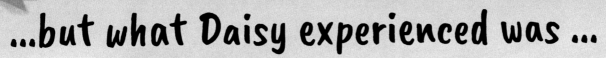

...but what Daisy experienced was ...

the continuous **ruckus** of students **destroying** every bit of happiness their teacher Ms Landon created and placed in their classroom.

Day after day she saw the same children rip the classroom books, throw materials across the room,

tear down the class learning off the walls, and even throw furniture.

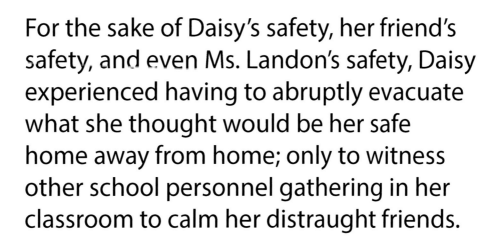

For the sake of Daisy's safety, her friend's safety, and even Ms. Landon's safety, Daisy experienced having to abruptly evacuate what she thought would be her safe home away from home; only to witness other school personnel gathering in her classroom to calm her distraught friends.

Daisy never imagined school being a place where she and her friends would miss out on so much learning, all because of her friends constant interruptions!

She never thought that other children her age could cause other children to be so unhappy.

What's worse, is that Daisy didn't have the words she needed to express what she was experiencing and feeling when she got home to her parents.

She didn't understand how she could have once pictured school as a place of fun with friends and her teacher, but now see it as …

A place of

fear ...

A place of

hurt ...

A place of
destruction ...

A place of
anger ...

A place of

confusion

about what is right
and wrong ...

and even a place of **disrespect ...**

So one day Daisy did what she loved most -

she wrote ...

She wrote a letter to her class and teacher describing how she was feeling as best as she could.

The next day, Daisy asked her teacher if she could read her letter aloud to the class.

Ms. Landon allowed her to do just that.

While trying to hold back tears,
she read ...

Every time you **slam** the door
you make me **jump**

because **I'm scared!**

Every time you say words
we aren't supposed to say,

it makes me angry!

Every time you destroy our classroom,

it makes me sad!

Every time you run through the halls of the school building,

it makes me feel disappointed!

Every time you stop Ms. Landon
from teaching,

it makes me feel empty!

Every time you hurt me or my friends,

I feel the need to keep them safe!

And **EVERY TIME** you've made
Ms. Landon cry,
I wished you would just

GO AWAY!

But you can't go away.

You can't go away because we are all supposed to be here together.

We are all supposed to feel **safe together**!

We are all supposed to **smile together**!

We are all supposed to **learn together**!

I want you to know that **EVERYTHING** you do in class that distracts us **takes away from our learning**;

not just in that moment, but for the rest of the day.

We only get one chance to make our time together this year perfect. How can we **un-do** this **un-perfect** year to make it a perfect one starting **NOW?**

Made in the USA
Monee, IL
11 July 2022

99288332R00029